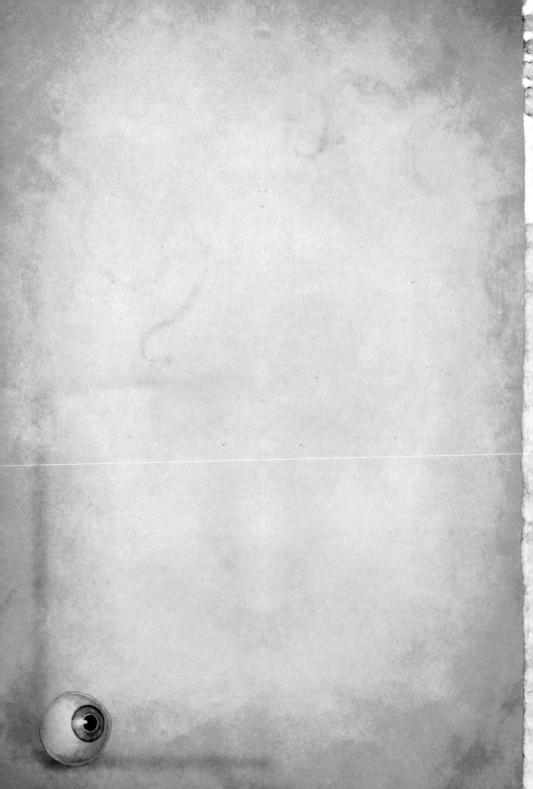

We R Igors

Enquiring Reader.

I have been asked to provide an introduction to this curious little tome.

When one has lived as long as I have, the notion of a diary covering just one year seems to me a little short-sighted and shows a certain lack of confidence in the future. But then who am I to judge, ve all have our own destiny. Indeed, in the case of the Igor Clan, a destiny that vill undoubtedly include many changes. The assiduous pursuit of self-improvement and abhorrence of vaste is the Igor's vay and I applaud them. I am sure both you and they vill find this diary of some value in the coming year; if only to record notable events and personal gains. As the Igors say 'vhat goes around comes around' and so please be kind to your Igor and and all of him vill be kind to you.

And now I hear my own dear Igor approaching my mausoleum, my cocoa in his hand; or, should I say, quite possibly someone else's hand, just as he has been doing for the last two hundred years and I shall retire to my coffin and rest upon the soil of the homeland. Unfortunately, the children of the night are suffering from a bout of distemper and are a little restless. I shall have to do something about them when I avake.

My very best vishes to you all,

Lady Margolotta Amaya Katerina Assumpta Crassina von Uberwald

January

M	T	W	T	F	S	S
			1	2	3	4
5	6	7	8	9	10	11
12	13	14	15	16	17	18
19	20	21	22	23	24	25
26	27	28	29	30	31	

February

M	T	W	T	F	S	S
						1
2	3	4	5	6	7	8
9	10	11	12	13	14	15
16	17	18	19	20	21	22
23	24	25	26	27	28	

March

M	T	W	T	F	S	S
						1
2	3	4	5	6	7	8
9	10	11	12	13	14	15
16	17	18	19	20	21	22
23/30	24/31	25	26	27	28	29

April

M	T	W	T	F	S	S
	1	2	3	4	5	
6	7	8	9	10	11	12
13	14	15	16	17	18	19
20	21	22	23	24	25	26
27	28	29	30			

May

M	T	W	T	F	S	S
				1	2	3
4	5	6	7	8	9	10
11	12	13	14	15	16	17
18	19	20	21	22	23	24
25	26	27	28	29	30	31

June

M	T	W	T	F	S	S
1	2	3	4	5	6	7
8	9	10	11	12	13	14
15	16	17	18	19	20	21
22	23	24	25	26	27	28
29	30					

July

M	T	W	T	F	S	S
		1	2	3	4	5
6	7	8	9	10	11	12
13	14	15	16	17	18	19
20	21	22	23	24	25	26
27	28	29	30	31		

Augutht

M	T	W	T	F	S	S
					1	2
3	4	5	6	7	8	9
10	11	12	13	14	15	16
17	18	19	20	21	22	23
24/31	25	26	27	28	29	30

Theptember

M	T	W	T	F	S	S
	1	2	3	4	5	6
7	8	9	10	11	12	13
14	15	16	17	18	19	20
21	22	23	24	25	26	27
28	29	30				

October

M	T	W	T	F	S	S
			1	2	3	4
5	6	7	8	9	10	11
12	13	14	15	16	17	18
19	20	21	22	23	24	25
26	27	28	29	30	31	

November

M	T	W	T	F	S	S
						1
2	3	4	5	6	7	8
9	10	11	12	13	14	15
16	17	18	19	20	21	22
23/30	24	25	26	27	28	29

Dethember

M	T	W	T	F	S	S
	1	2	3	4	5	6
7	8	9	10	11	12	13
14	15	16	17	18	19	20
21	22	23	24	25	26	27
28	29	30	31			

We R Igors

A SPARE HAND WHEN NEEDED

THE OLD RATHAUS · BAD SCHÜSCHEIN · UBERWALD

NAME: ....

ADDRESS: ....

Age: .... *(age of oldest part if different)* .... Title/s: ....
Occupation: ....
Manual Skills: ....
Dominant Hand: *Left:* .... *Right:* .... *Sometimes:* .... *Other:* ....

NEXT OF KIN
Name: ....
Address: ....
....

LEGAL REPRESENTATIVE
Name: ....
Address: ....
....

PLEASE ANSWER THE FOLLOWING QUESTIONS IN ORDER THAT ANY BEQUESTS
YOU HAVE MADE CAN BE HONOURED.

HAVE YOU MADE A WILL?

Details of any bequests involving your body parts:
....
....
....
....

OTHER POSSIBLE CALLS ON YOUR PARTS:
*Details of any promises made to family
members, friends, loan companies, casinos,
organisations (inc. clubs), wagers or workmates:*
....
....
....

IN ORDER THAT WE CAN ACHIEVE AN OPTIMAL BENEFIT FROM YOUR DONATION
WE REQUEST THAT YOU COMPLETE THE FOLLOWING QUESTIONNAIRE.

BODY CONDITION & GENERAL FITNESS

ALCOHOL CONSUMPTION	SMOKER: TOBACCO (1)	OTHER: (2) *Mind Altering Substances Etc.*
None:	None:	None: ....
Moderate:	Moderate:	Moderate: ....
Lots:	Lots:	Lots: ....

LIMBS AND EXTREMITIES

HANDS:
Left: Original ...... / Other ......
Right: Original ...... / Other ......

KNEES:
Left: Original ...... / Other ......
Right: Original ...... / Other ......

HIPS:
Left: Original ...... / Other ......
Right: Original ...... / Other ......

FEET:
Left: Original ...... / Other ......
Right: Original ...... / Other ......

FINGERS (L): 1/2/3/4/5/6/7/8/9/10/*Thumb/other* ....
FINGERS (R): 1/2/3/4/5/6/7/8/9/10/*Thumb/other* ....
TOES (L): 1/2/3/4/5/6/7/8/9/10/*other* ....
TOES (R): 1/2/3/4/5/6/7/8/9/10/*other* ....

OTHER PARTS:

HEART: *Original: .... / Other: ....*
LUNGS: *Original: .... / Other: ....*
KIDNEYS: *Original: ...... / Other: ....*
STOMACH: *Original: ..... / Other: ....*
WATER WORKS:
Original: .... / Other: ....
RECREATIONAL ORGANS:
Original: .... / Other: ....

PLEASE MARK IN THE SPACES PROVIDED

C-MAIL: YETHMARTHTER UBERWALD

I HEREBY DECLARE THAT THE INFORMATION I HAVE GIVEN
IS TRUE AS FAR AS I CAN ASCERTAIN.

In the event of my death through natural causes, accident, trauma, act of war, crime or act of gods, any useful body parts or organs may be removed from my remains by an accredited member of the Igor Assurance Company as soon as death has been certified by a qualified independent medical practitioner.

I further declare that should my remains or any part thereof be deemed unsuitable for reallocation due to trauma, disease or parasitical infestation, then the removal and disposal of such residue shall be the responsibility of my next of kin.

Signed (or mark): ....

In the presence of witness

Name: .... Signature: ....

 FINALLY, PLEASE COMPLETE THE ATTACHED DONOR CARD AND KEEP IT
ABOUT YOUR PERSON AT ALL TIMES.

Cut (carefully) along the dotted line.

DONOR CARD

NAME: ....

ADDRESS: ....

....

NEXT OF KIN: ....

I confirm that being of sound mind and body I bequeath my mortal remains to the **We R Igors** Organisation that they may transplant or reallocate any part of my cadaver to any recipient whose life it will enhance. In addition they may remove and preserve or freeze any part for use at a future date.

CLACKS:
IGR-III
A-M

We R Igors

CLACKS:
IGR-III
A-M

ELM STREET, ANKH-MORPORK

Thurthday

January 1tht

New Year'th Day
Hogswatchday (ICK)

Friday

Thaturday

Thunday

Thayingth from the Old Country

Alwayth let the left hand know what the right hand'th doing, wherever it ith.

Monday

Tuethday

Wednethday

Thurthday

Friday

January **9**th

Thaturday

January **10**th

Thunday

January **11**th

Octeday

Although many citizens have good reason to be grateful to the Igor clan, recruitment to the donor card scheme often requires a certain amount of encouragement. The official We R Igors enrolment campaign has yielded mixed results.

Monday

January 12th

Tuethday

January 13th

Wednethday

January 14th

Thurthday

January 15th

Friday

January 16th

Thaturday

January 17th

Thunday

January 18th

Octeday

We're all familiar with the Igors' penchant for self-improvement. It is important, however, to remember that it is very much a relative term. It depends entirely on the 'self' in question and, indeed, on their definition of 'improvement'.

Monday

January 19th

Tuethday

January 20th

Wednethday

January 21tht

Thurthday

January 22nd

Friday

January 23rd

Thaturday

January 24th

Thunday

January 25th

Burnth Night

Octeday

Igor Hall of Fame
Field of Forensic Investigation

They say crime doesn't pay, but with a top Watch salary and access to all the 'thpareth' he could want, Igor would have to disagree. The Ankh-Morpork City Watch — the cutting edge of forensic science where Igor always gets his man/dwarf/golem/vampire/zombie/troll/banshee/goblin/etc.

Monday

Australia Day (Aus)
Anniversary Day (NZ)

January 26th

Tuethday

Holocaust Memorial Day

January 27th

Wednethday

January 28th

Thurthday

January 29th

Friday

Thaturday

TO: WE R IGORS
ANKH-MORPORK BRANCH, ELM STREET

CC: WE R IGORS
THE OLD RATHAUS, BAD SCHÜSCHEIN, UBERWALD

SIR,
    SOME OF YOUR COUNTRYMEN HAVE TAKEN TO NAILING THEIR 'LIGHTNING DEVICES' TO CLACKS TOWERS, ESPECIALLY THOSE IN HIGH PLACES. THESE CONTRAPTIONS ARE CAUSING SERIOUS PROBLEMS IN OUR WORKING ENVIRONMENT, AND WHILE AN IGOR (IF PRESENT) CAN OFTEN RESUSCITATE OUR EMPLOYEES, THEY ARE NOT ALWAYS ABLE TO REPAIR TOOLS OR, INDEED, THE CLACKS MACHINERY WHICH HAS OFTEN BEEN DAMAGED BEYOND REPAIR. ADDITIONALLY, CASUALTIES FROM UNSCHEDULED LIGHTNING STRIKES ARE TAKING THEIR TOLL AND THE ENGINEERS OFTEN REFUSE TO WORK IN STORMY CONDITIONS.
    WOULD YOU KINDLY INFORM YOUR MEMBERS THAT CLACKS TOWERS ARE PRIVATE PROPERTY AND THE ADDITION OF ANY MAST OR DEVICE IS STRICTLY FORBIDDEN.
    YOURS TRULY,
    VERA PONY. DEPT. OF HEALTH AND SAFETY, GRAND TRUNK CO.

Contract of Employment

Note: This is a full employment Servant/Master contract

Name and address of employer/Not Mad Scientist:

....

.... (Title/s) ....

The Igor known as Igor agrees to serve the aforementioned family/individual/entity/Not Mad Scientist henceforth to be addressed as Marthter/Mithtreth for a period of .... months/years or until such service is mutually terminated *(see clause 1)*.

The Igor will receive a remittance of .... to be paid monthly as stipend in general, coin of the realm, or banker's draft.

It is mutually agreed that said Igor is hired locatio conductio operarum and/or locatio conductio operis to fulfil the following functions in strict accordance with the Code of the Igors *(addendum 1)*.

For the purposes of this contract the duties of the aforementioned Igor are as follows:

1 Domestic: to include butler, footman, valet, gentleman's gentleman, cook and such duties that may fall within this station. This includes the traditional domestic skills of dust-laying, door hinge erosion, floor board squeaking, candle dribbling and cutting eyeholes in family portraits. Also, when appropriate, to provide a regular supply of well sieved 'soil of the homeland' *(see also clause 2)*.

2 Work Place: to include assistance with forensic, medical, chemical and biological research and experimentation. To provide expertise in all these fields and have the skills to create such equipment as the processes require *(see clause 3)*.

3 Procurement: the acquisition (at a reasonable price when necessary) of such items, materials, parts or services that may be required in pursuit of any of the activities listed above.

Clause 1: Should the employer or any member of their family, household, or workplace cause a malicious civic disturbance (see clause 1a) the result of which is a move to evict the family from, or destroy, their property, or cause the cessation of any activity or process which could result in injury to Igor or loss of his belongings then the contract is deemed in breach.

Clause 1a: For the purposes of this contract a civic disturbance is defined as the gathering of three or more individuals having about their persons such articles as pitchforks and/or other agricultural/domestic implements capable of inflicting injury. This also includes persons holding torches or other combustible devices with the express intent of igniting person or property.

Clause 2: Not to include, unless mutually agreed, the cleaning of pens, kennels and feeding bowls, or the bagging up and disposal of any excreta.

Clause 3: Technical skills to include glassblowing, mechanical engineering, preservation, chemical analysis, limb and organ transplants and full-body reanimation.

Igor Zero Hours Contract

Zero-hours contracts are available for functions, sudden sawmill/windmill incidents, immediate regeneration or reanimation projects, unexpected visitors, or any other reason why an Igor may be needed on an ad hoc basis.

Our organization can despatch an Igor to any location by rail, post or carrier from one of our many branch offices. All that is required is a banker's draft to be lodged with our office as a holding non-returnable deposit and your requirements for an immediate placement will be speedily fulfilled.

Apply by Clacks to Head Office for details and availability.

Igors: A Spare Hand When Needed.

ADDENDUM
THE CODE OF THE IGORS:

AN IGOR NEVER CONTRADICTS.

AN IGOR NEVER COMPLAINS.

AN IGOR NEVER PASSES JUDGEMENT.

AN IGOR NEVER MAKES ANY PERSONAL
REMARKS ABOUT HIS EMPLOYER.

AN IGOR NEVER ASKS QUESTIONS.

AN IGOR WILL BE AVAILABLE AT ALL
HOURS OF THE DAY OR NIGHT.

AN IGOR ANTICIPATES;
THE DOORBELL NEVER RINGS.

Thunday

Beating the Bounds (Plunkers)
Doodling Day

Thayingth from the Old Country

Beware old headth
on young thoulderth.

Monday
Imbolc (Candlemas)

February 2nd

Tuethday

February 3rd

Wednethday

February 4th

Thurthday

February 5th

Friday

Accession of Queen Elizabeth II
Waitangi Day (NZ)

Thaturday

February 7th

Thunday

February 8th

Octeday

When considering a position with one of our esteemed lupine friends, one must remember to take the rough with the smooth. They do tend to be very loyal employers with a keen sense of tradition, but as the old saying goes 'Thome little jobth for the marthter are methier than otherth'.

Monday

Tuethday

Wednethday

Thurthday

Friday

February 13th

Thaturday

February 14th

Tht. Valentine'th Day

Thunday

February 15th

Thayingth from the Old Country

The way to a man'th heart ith up and under hith ribcage.

Monday

President's Day (USA)

February 16th

Tuethday

Shrove Tuesday, Pancake Day, Fat Tuesday, Mardi Gras (USA)

February 17th

Wednethday

February 18th

Thurthday

February 19th

Friday
February 20th

Thaturday
February 21tht

Thunday
February 22nd

Octeday

Igor Hall of Fame
Field of Equine Development

Although he remains a fixture of Hobson's Livery Yard, Igor officially retired after his horse 'I Got a Hunch' won the Grand Rust Cup by a nose.

Monday

February 23rd

Tuethday

February 24th

Auditors' Day

Wednethday

February 25th

Thurthday

February 26th

Friday

Thaturday

February 28th

Thunday

March 1tht

Tht. David'th Day

Octeday

Ath they thay in the Old Country 'If you don't want the monthter, don't pull the lever'.

Monday
Labour Day (WA)

March 2nd

Tuethday

March 3rd

Wednethday

March 4th

Thurthday

March 5th

Friday

Thaturday

Thunday

Daylight Saving Time begins (USA & Canada)

Thayingth from the Old Country

He who pickth hith own nothe, getth the profile he detherveth.

Monday

Commonwealth Day
Labour Day (Vic, Tas)
Canberra Day (ACT)
Eight Hours Day (Tas)

March 9th

Tuethday

March 10th

Wednethday

March 11th

Thurthday

March 12th

Friday

Thaturday

Thunday

Octeday

PUBLIC THERVITH

'Igor'th Thpareth & Repairth' cabins have become a common sight around the logging camps of the lower Ramtops. Whether you need a quick tune-up, a full service or their legendary 'while you wait' part exchange, an Igor is always on hand, with often more than just a hand.

Monday

Tuethday

Tht. Patrick'th Day

Wednethday

Thurthday

Friday

Thaturday

March 21tht

Thunday

March 22nd

Octeday

IT'TH ALL IN THE THMALL PRINT

When locals start asking awkward questions like "What's that strange glow?", "What's all this maniacal laughter about, then?" and "Why exactly is there a laboratory in dat old goffic castle?", you know that the next question comes with a pitchfork at the end. It's a constant comfort to know that every Igor's contract of employment includes a 'get-out' clause as standard.

Monday

March **23**rd

Tuethday

March **24**th

Wednethday

March **25**th

Thurthday

March **26**th

Friday

Thaturday

Thunday

Octeday

KEEPING UP APPEARANCES

Nothing ties a room together like a well-constructed coating of dust. Accents of cobweb and discreet bloodstains are all well and good, but be sure to apply a generous foundation of coarse dust for that ultra-natural look (cellar/crypt-sourced is recommended), and why not set it off with a liberal layer of attic-grade particles?

Monday

March 30th

Tuethday

March 31tht

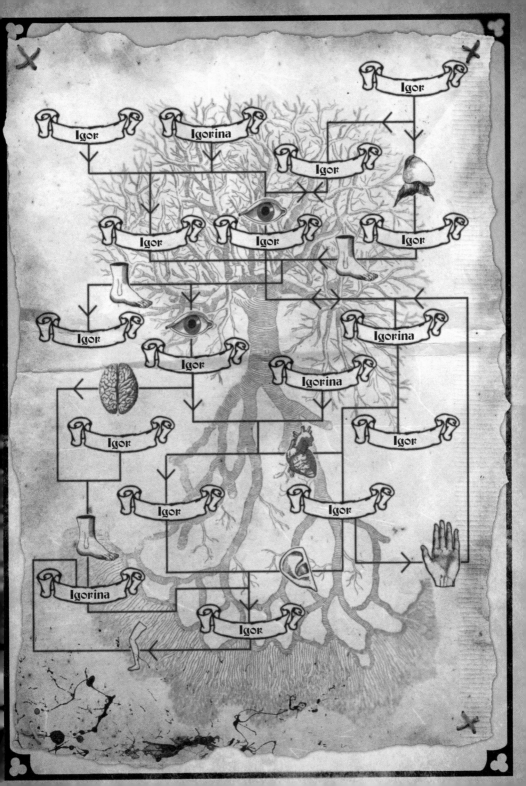

Guild of Embalmers, Peach Pie Street, Ankh-Morpork
To Lord Vetinari, Patrician of Ankh-Morpork

Your Lordship,

We respectfully ask for your help in addressing a problem arising from the activities of a new immigrant population in our city. Increasingly we find that we are preserving and burying incomplete bodies rather than the whole cadaver. Often by the time we've pulled our black hats on to go and visit a recently bereaved family some keen young Igor has been there before us and removed choice parts from the body. In many cases the remainder is not even identifiable as the named deceased and there is not enough to embalm. The bits and pieces rattle around in a coffin unless carefully packed in straw and we are often obliged to use sand to make the weight up. Further more, there have been occasions when our skilled operatives have arrived to find the dearly departed drinking tea with a happy Igor who has brought said deceased back to life.

We are not saying that the Igors are not good people, in fact our own members benefit from their attentions and speedy replacements following injuries from saw or shovel. However we have a living to make, my Lord, and this haphazard overturning of burial rites and traditions must be addressed.

We eagerly await your reply,

Yours sincerely,
Oscar Venting, Guild President

Wednethday

April 1tht

April Fool'th Day

Thurthday

April 2nd

Friday

April 3rd
Good Friday

Thaturday

April 4th
Eathter Saturday

Thunday

April 5th
Eathter Thunday
Daylight Savings Time ends (NZ & Aus)

Octeday

Monday

April 6th

Eathter Monday (Bank Holiday: England, Wales & N. Ireland)
Declaration of Arbroath (Scotland)

Tuethday

April 7th

Wednethday

April 8th

Thurthday

April 9th

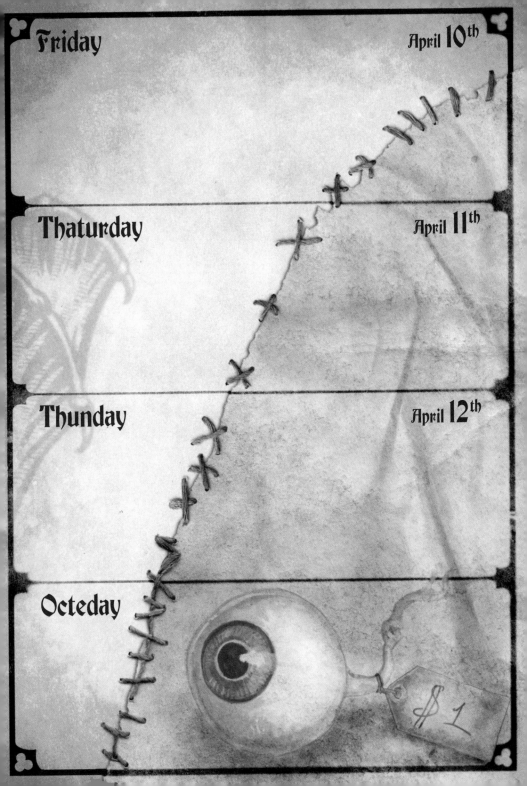

Friday   April 10th

Thaturday   April 11th

Thunday   April 12th

Octeday

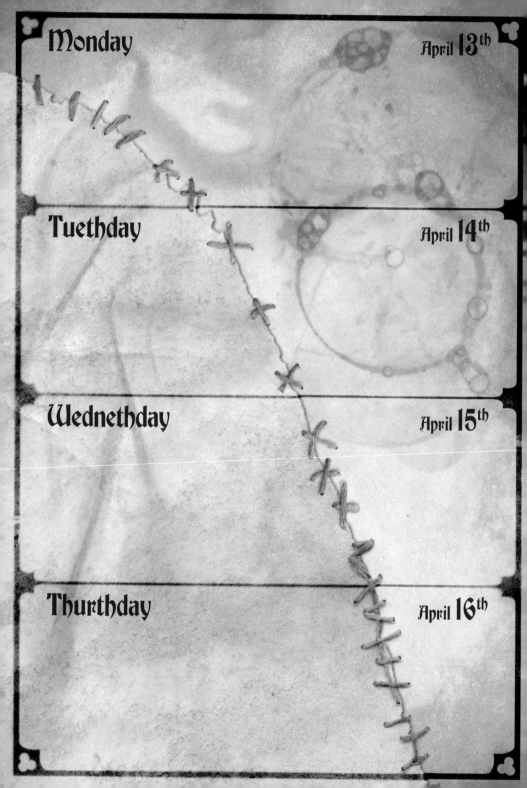

Monday   April **13**th

Tuethday   April **14**th

Wednethday   April **15**th

Thurthday   April **16**th

Friday

Thaturday

April **18**th

Thunday

April **19**th

Octeday

IGORINA HALL OF FAME
Field of Public Service

Aunt Igorina, the brains* behind We R Igors, is responsible
for the largest single Clacks-order organisation in Uberwald.
They can send anything from a size 4 pinkie to a full
complement of Igor assistants anywhere in the known world.

*and everything else

Monday

Tuethday
The Queen's Birthday

April 21tht

Wednethday

April 22nd

Thurthday
Tht. George'th Day

April 23rd

Friday

April 24th

Thaturday

April 25th

ANZAC Day

Thunday

April 26th

Octeday

IGOR HALL OF FAME
Field of Enterprise & Diversification

The breakdown of a relationship, a dyslexic artist, yer dear old mum finding out — there are many reasons to regret a tattoo. Thankfully, Igor's Tattoo Removal Clinic on Morpork Docks can make life just that little bit easier. His 'Wedding Night Special' has meant countless 'Marys' throughout the city, remain blissfully unaware of all the previous 'Mildreds'.

Monday April **27**th

Tuethday April **28**th

Creator's Birthday

Wednethday April **29**th

Thurthday April **30**th

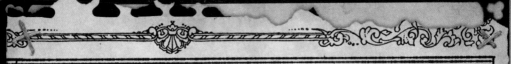

Thpecialitht Interetht

PETS

Hambits.
First generation cross. 4 weeks old and free to good homes.
Contact Igor, Morry Rd. AM

Ear-mouse, ready for transplant.
Apply We R Igors, Elm Street.

Three-legged Lurcher needs good home.
Suit one-legged man.

LONELY HEARTS

Lonely heart seeks a body for lasting relationship.

Igor seeks companion for mutual improvement and musical evenings.

Dethperately theeking thole mate.
Thole needed for left foot.
Apply Igor, 16, Unmet End, Ankh-Morpork.

GENERAL

Free Range Feet.
No corns or bunions. Various sizes.
Available now.

Suck it and See.
Temporary oral transplants.

Unexpectedly available.
Good working colon.
Details on request.

Do you have problems with in-growing toenails?
Let us give you new toes.

Mobile ice house for sale.
Ideal for Rapid Response Igor.
Apply The Brindisi Ice Cream Company, Miracle Yard.

Thumb needed.
Must have good nail.

The Myrtle Street Igorina Clinic for the Self-Made Woman.
Head to toe alterations.

Crowning Glory,
Lungent Lane.

Igorina Hair and Scalp Clinic.
'Living Wigs', the ultimate hair-extension now available!

The Ankh-Morpork Butchery School and Abattoir, needs part-time Igor – good wages and weekend joint, split shifts.

Let us help you find your perfect nose.
Plenty to pick from at our cold store in Elm Street.

Stump Removal.
Discreet service.

Genuine soil of the Homeland.
Dried and sieved. Buyer collect.
Kings Industrial Estate, New Ankh.

LOST AND FOUND

Lost in Filigree Street area.
Single brown lace-up (size 9) with foot.
Contact Arthur Skuttle, Can't Find It Street.

Found on Nap Hill:
Single knitted red glove with index finger.
Contact Mrs Wedge, Lum-Snippet Lane, Ankh-Morpork.

Found on The Brass Bridge.
Approx twelve ft of lower intestine (human) and a kidney.
Available for quick transplant if unclaimed.

Lost in Mended Drum last Saturday night. Right eye, left ear and several teeth.
If found return to Arthur Smallbeam c/o The Lady Sybil Free Hospital.

EXCHANGE

Body and Sole Clinic,
Dimwell Street, AM.
Exchange left foot for right foot Size 8.

One brown and one blue eye.
Exchange either to get a matching pair.
Igor, c/o We R Igors Elm Street.

Eye for an eye, tooth for a tooth. Easy going terms on like for like. Cash paid.
Igor, c/o Guild of Embalmers and Allied Tradesmen.

Arms and navels surplus store.
Two for one on navels, includes fitting. Forearm exchange program available.
Groyling Street.

Spleen, good condition, one careful owner and she only took it to church on Octedays.
Will swap for knuckles, toes or particularly nice knees.
Contact Igor, c/o 41 High Dukes

THPOT THE BALL

WRITE TO REPLY

SIR,

The blessings of Om be upon all who read this epistle.

It has come to our attention that some members of our congregation have subscribed to a movement called the Igor Assurance Group. It is my duty to remind them that it is written in the ninth book of Ossary, chapter vii, verse 23: *"Yay, and the whole body will be resurrected even from dust and the Mighty Om shall gather all of his faithful together, reunited under his benevolent and eternal gaze"*.

This glorious resurrection is going to be very difficult for those who, having received a kidney from Quirm and a replacement knee from an address in Dolly Sisters, have finally been scattered far and wide across the Sto Plains. The benefits of full bodily resurrection and eternal life could be seriously compromised by the haphazard redistribution of limbs and organs throughout a heathen population.

On a practical note; an eternity spent with one hand, no eyes, and half a leg could be singularly unrewarding.

Yours in Om's Blessings,
REVEREND TOBIAS GULLET
Minister in residence,
The Reformed Temple of Om,
Demon Fly Street, Ankh-Morpork.

SIR,

I am a well-known and respected citizen of Ankh-Morpork and I am always willing to do my duty for our Great City; being dead is no bar to civic responsibility. However I am seriously concerned that what has been a gateway to eternal citizenship for some of us is now under threat. Resurrection requires a whole mind and body; it cannot be done when vital organs and random appendages have been removed.

I would like to remind the Igor clan that there are different ways of living and while my associates and I appreciate their enthusiasm for self-improvement and life extension, I would respectfully ask that they please respect our traditions. We like the way we are and do not appreciate attempts at *'making us better'* however well-meaning they may be.

Yours faithfully,
REG SHOE
The Fresh Start Club,
668, Elm Street, Ankh-Morpork.

Friday

Thaturday

May **2**nd

Thunday

May **3**rd

DEAR THUR,
   We are very thorry that the activitieth of our clan have cauthed dithtreth among the thitithenth of Ankh-Morpork. Our intention ith to thave life where we can but it theemth that the tendenthy of theveral of our young and enthuthiathtic memberth to dive in and athk quethtionth later hath created thome bad feeling. We have taken thtepth to enthure that thith will not happen again.
   Yourth truly,
WE R IGORS, *Elm St., Ankh-Morpork.*

Monday
Early May Bank Holiday (UK)
Labour Day (NT)

May 4th

Tuethday

May 5th

Wednethday

May 6th

Thurthday

May 7th

Friday

Thaturday

Thunday

Mother'th Day (USA, Aus & NZ)

Octeday

Surprisingly, people don't often ask questions about the love lives of Igors. They certainly appear to be rather lucky in love. Dark rumours of bespoke brides, maids to measure and, worse still, 'up-cycling' abound. The truth of the matter is that the phrase, 'darlink, I can change', really does mean something to an Igor.

Monday

May 11th

Tuethday

May 12th

Wednethday

May 13th

Thurthday

May 14th

Friday

Thaturday

Thunday

Octeday

Igor Hall of Fame
Field of Cosmetic Surgery

The 'A Stitch in Time' cosmetic surgery clinic certainly raised a few eyebrows in Ankh-Morpork when it opened its doors in the Year of the Reversed Ptarmigan. People now travel from all over the Sto Plains to discreetly cheat the ravages of time and put right the subtle mistakes their creator saw fit to bestow upon them.

Monday

Tuethday

May 19th

Wednethday

May 20th

Thurthday

May 21tht

Friday

May 22nd

Thaturday

May 23rd

Thunday

May 24th

Octeday

People say that brainwashing is a long and difficult process. In reality, it's all about conditioning. Igor's patented three step program will have you pure of mind in no time: 'lather, rinthe, repeat' — just don't forget the golden rule: 'ALWAYTH label the bowlth.'

Monday

Glorious Twenty-Fifth of May
Spring Bank Holiday
Memorial Day (USA)

May **25**th

Tuethday

May **26**th

Wednethday

May **27**th

Thurthday

May **28**th

Friday

May 29th

Thaturday

May 30th

Thunday

May 31tht

Octeday

THTITCHED UP

A keen understanding of the human form coupled with exceptional needlework has led to a long and respected tradition of Igor tailors. Despite their skill, trade is still predominantly 'for Igors, by Igors', the general populace being somewhat wary of any Igor offering cut price 'alterations' wanting to know their exact measurements.

Monday

The Queen's Birthday (NZ)
Western Australia Day

June 1tht

Tuethday

Coronation Day (UK)

June 2nd

Wednethday

June 3rd

Thurthday

June 4th

Friday

June 5th

Thaturday

June 6th

Thunday

June 7th

Octeday

On 'Getting Better'

When seeking treatment from an Igor, it is important to specify whether one wishes to get well, or get better. A case in point being Mr Schlutz of Glitz (pictured), who only went to Igor for an ingrown toenail. Most inhabitants of Far Uberwald know the importance of clarity in such matters, and only the loneliest souls with no one to warn them tend to get caught out these days*.

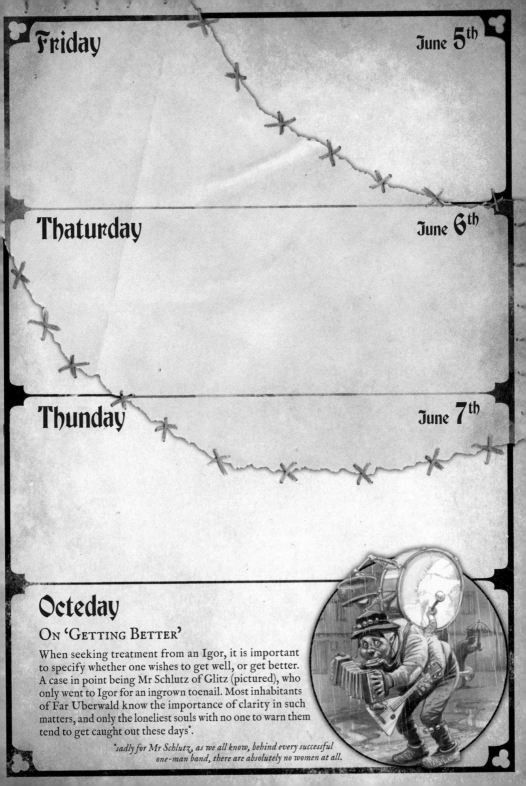

*sadly for Mr Schlutz, as we all know, behind every successful one-man band, there are absolutely no women at all.

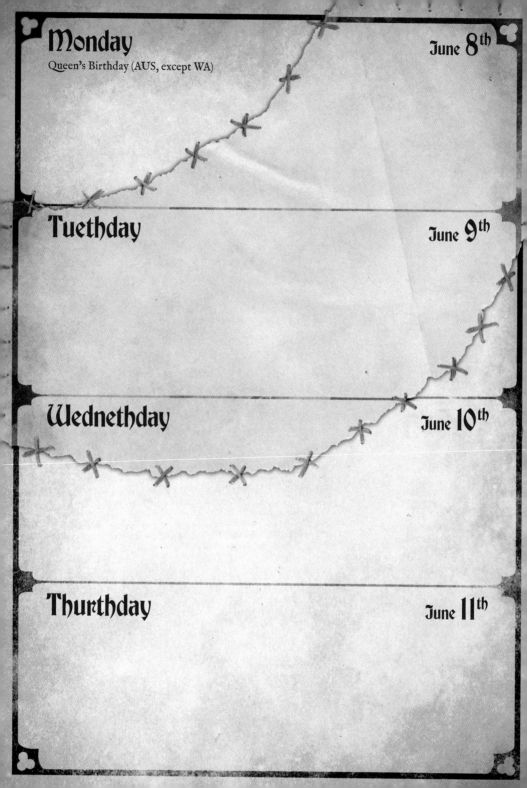

Monday
Queen's Birthday (AUS, except WA)

June 8th

Tuethday

June 9th

Wednethday

June 10th

Thurthday

June 11th

Friday

Thaturday

Thunday

Octeday

Uberwald is well known for its 'psychotropic atmosphere'*. You don't get away with saying something like "I zink it came from ... ze castle ..." without hearing a hearty clap of thunder or foreboding howl. Igors learnt long ago to harness the power of these bolts from the blue, just don't shake hands with them afterwards.

*like pathetic fallacy, but less pathetic.

Monday

June 15th

Tuethday

June 16th

Wednethday

June 17th

Thurthday

June 18th

Small Gods' Eve

Friday

Thaturday

June 20th

Thunday

June 21tht
Father'th Day (UK, USA, Canada)
Litha (Summer Solstice)

Octeday

IGOR HALL OF FAME
Field of Optometry

This young Igor revolutionised the world of optometry with the invention of 40/40 vision. One of a few second (approximately) generation Morporkian Igors, he is said to have inherited his father's forward-thinking attitude and his mother's eyes.

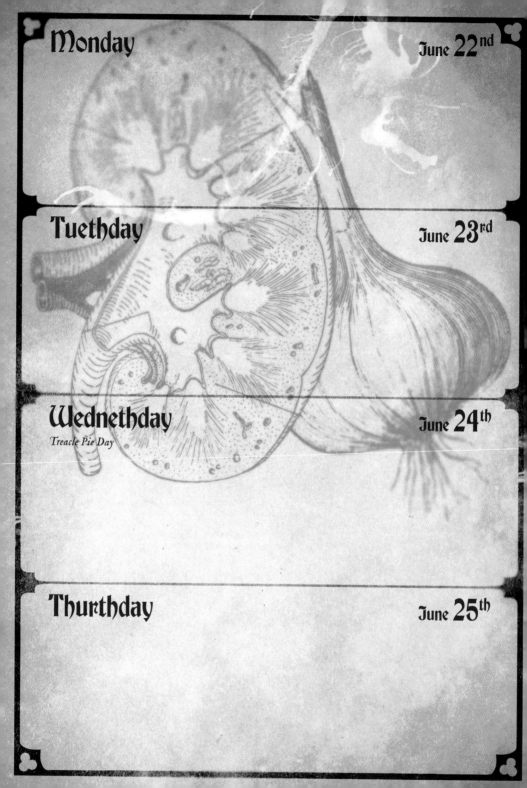

Monday

June 22nd

Tuethday

June 23rd

Wednethday

Treacle Pie Day

June 24th

Thurthday

June 25th

Friday

June 26th

Thaturday

June 27th

Wizards' Excuse-Me

Thunday

June 28th

Octeday

Igor Hall of Fame
Field of Botany

Many people talk to their plants, but of all those who elicit
a response only a very special few are afforded the luxury
of being allowed out in public. In Igor's case however, he
was awarded an honorary doctorate in Unnatural Sciences.
He was also the creator of the very first age-restricted tomatoes,
being, as they were, incredibly saucy.

Monday
June 29th

Tuethday
June 30th

To: We R Igors
Ankh-Morpork Branch, Elm Street

Cc: We R Igors
The Old Rathaus, Bad Schüschein, Uberwald

Enthusiasm and the desire for improvement is something we all laud in the young and inexperienced Igor, but we are dismayed to be receiving reports of unseemly scuffles at the scenes of accidents throughout the great city of Ankh-Morpork. There is in our psyche the need to harvest and not be wasteful of useful parts that the recently deceased has no further use for, but the young person who ran off with a horse's hind leg, a dog's head, a cat's ears and tail and the coachman's left foot is clearly taking things too far. This practice must cease immediately and the written permission of next of kin, or owner in the case of an animal or undead, must be obtained before harvesting commences.

RECOVERY POSITIONS

FOR OPTIMUM RECOVERY OF PARTS THE FOLLOWING GUIDE HELPS REDUCE WASTAGE AND TRAUMA AND GIVES CLEAR ACCESS TO THE PRIMARY GOALS.

THE SUPINE RECOVERY POSITION

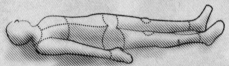

The Supine Recovery Position is recommended for facial features (apart from ears), the heart, lungs, liver, stomach and intestine.

Hip and knee joints may also be recovered in this position though there is a school of thought which suggests that a complete arm or leg is more easily detached from the side. Extremities can be recovered from the whole limb once you are back in your laboratory.

THE PRONE RECOVERY POSITION

Use the prone recovery position for extraction of kidneys, removal of the complete spine as well as individual vertebrae.

To extract the contents of the cranial cavity, including eyes attached to optic nerves and all ENT parts, it is recommended that the head is removed and taken straight to the laboratory for completion of the procedure.

Experience has taught us that it is important to be prepared.

The casual transporting of body parts, particularly heads, in wheelbarrows or open boxes attracts unwanted attention. There are now available any number of discreet insulated recovery containers, being waterproof, strong and designed for discrete purpose with special 'eye-cups' and small compartments for keeping delicate organs undamaged.

Bio-Artificing

ARE YOU TIRED OF WAITING FOR THE RIGHT NOSE TO COME AROUND?

ARE YOU FED UP WITH THE WRONG-SIZED FINGERS AND BADLY MATCHING EARS?

We can now offer a service second to none with our amazing new and hygienic process. *Bio-Artificing offers unblemished features, grown to order, designed to fit and guaranteed for life.*

For a FREE CONSULTATION visit the NEW IGOR CLINIC, RESTITUTION ROAD, ANKH-MORPORK.

Wednethday

Canada Day (Canada)

July 1^{tht}

Thurthday

July 2nd

Friday

Thaturday

July 4th

Independence Day (USA)

Thunday

July 5th

Octeday

Monday

Patrician's Day

July 6th

Tuethday

July 7th

Wednethday

July 8th

Thurthday

July 9th

Friday
July 10th

Thaturday
July 11th

Thunday
July 12th

Battle of the Boyne (Bank Holiday in N. Ireland)

Octeday

The Ear-mouse is just of the many new 'beathtieth' appearing as a by-product of bio-artificing. Nosey the rat and Lippy the frog are also contributing, in their own way, to this new science. Testing on animals somehow seems more sporting; a radish can't run away.

Monday

July 13th

Tuethday

July 14th

Bastille Day

Wednethday

July 15th

Thurthday

July 16th

Friday

Thaturday

Thunday

Octeday

A delivery from We R Igors, ready to take up his new position. When an Igor finds himself, *bynofaultofhisown*, between 'marthterth', We R Igors will find him a suitable 'plathement' according to his skills, references and disposition. Courtesy Igors are available in the event of a breakdown.

Monday

July 20th

Tuethday

July 21tht

Wednethday

Uberwald League of Temperance Day: Remember: Not One Drop!

July 22nd

Thurthday

July 23rd

Friday

July **24**th

Thaturday

July **25**th

Thunday

July **26**th

Mizzling Sunday

Octeday

The medical profession as a whole*, are doubtless indebted to the expertise of the Igors. Given a choice, however, modern clinics will tend to go with the services of the Igorina every time. The stitching is neater, maniacal laughter tends to be at a minimum and they don't take their work home with them.

*not to mention their long-suffering patients.

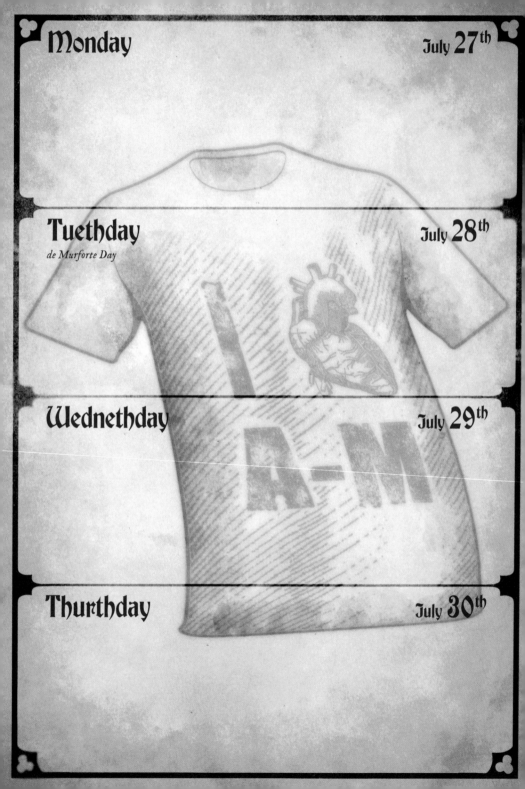

Monday   July **27**th

Tuethday   July **28**th
de Murforte Day

Wednethday   July **29**th

Thurthday   July **30**th

Rapid Response

A cry of pain, a scream of anguish, the dread sound of crashing carriages, the clash of steel on steel will bring the Rapid Response Igor rushing to the scene. Pushing his well-equipped cart through the streets and alleys of Ankh-Morpork the Independent Igor provides succour and healing where possible, and a speedy and clean removal of debris where not. These peripatetic Igors are kitted out for every emergency with a complete first (and last) aid kit including all the apparatus needed to repair broken bones, stitch wounds and even, where necessary, replace bespoke limbs. Never before in Ankh-Morpork have casualties been provided with such a quick and effective resolution of their injuries. This new service in the city has met with a mixed response from the citizens. Those of a silicon persuasion ignore it altogether and the dwarf community take a dubious view of the activities of Igors in general. But for the rest (with the exception of members of some religions) it is regarded as a boon and shows the forward looking attitude of Ankh-Morpork residents to 'cutting edge' medicine. As the Igor's are wont to say: 'What goeth around cometh around and thometimeth goeth around very fartht'.

WELCOME TO
ANKH-MORPORK
We R Igors
ELM STREET, ANKH-MORPORK

IF YOU ARE NEW TO ANKH-MORPORK* THE INFORMATION PRESENTED IN THIS LEAFLET WILL HELP YOU TO EQUIP YOUR OWN LABORATORY AND STORAGE FACILITY.

ICE SUPPLIES:

☞ The Igor Co-operative Ice Company (Icey Eye) import bulk ice from the Hub and then distribute from their storage facility in Elm Street. The ice is exceptionally clean and free from sediment and biological contamination.

APPARATUS:

☞ Scientific glassware, stands and clamps, balances and incubators are available from Assay & Decant, Five and Seven Yard, Ankh-Morpork.

☞ Bespoke glassware designed and produced by Drench and Gobby 3b, Street of The Cunning Artificers.

BOTTLED LIGHTNING:

☞ For the Igor in a hurry. Lighten Your Darkness, 14, The Mawnings, off Attic Bee Street.

METAL SMELTERS AND CASTERS:
(lead, zinc, copper iron etc.)

☞ Ingotsson's Works, Kings Industrial Estate, New Ankh.

CHEMICAL REAGENTS:

☞ The Ugli Acid Bath and Restraint Co. Glemious Wharf, Ankh-Morpork.

PROTECTIVE CLOTHING:
(aprons, tubing, rubber mats goggles etc.)

☞ Sonky Brothers, Monkey Street, Ankh-Morpork.

RECOVERY EQUIPMENT:
(Insulated boxes and bags, covered trolleys. Strong, waterproof and washable. All sizes).

☞ Sturdy & Shunt, Minting Trench Lane, Ankh-Morpork

SPARE PARTS:

Until you build up your own stock you may have access to the 'Surplus Store' located in the Elm Street icehouse. However, it is expected that once established, you will replace any items used, for the benefit of other clan members.

Please read the document entitled *An Igor's Guide to Behaviour in an Urban Environment* carefully. The guidelines are there for your own protection as well as the reputation of the Igor Clan.

* *'The Compleat Ankh-Morpork' is a comprehensive Guide to the City and includes street maps and a directory of traders and services. A reference copy is available in our library.*

Die and let live.

Thaturday

Augutht 1ᵗʰᵗ
Lammas (Lughnasadh)

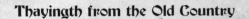

Thunday

Augutht 2ⁿᵈ

Thayingth from the Old Country

Keep a finger in every pie and alwayth keep an ear to the ground.

Monday

Summer Bank Holiday (Scotland), August Bank Holiday (Rep. of Ireland)

Augutht **3**rd

Tuethday

Augutht **4**th

Wednethday

Augutht **5**th

Thurthday

Augutht **6**th

Friday

Augutht 7th

Thaturday

Augutht 8th

Thunday

Augutht 9th

Octeday

'You rang, thur?'

Monday

Summer Bank Holiday (Scotland), August Bank Holiday (Rep. of Ireland)

Tuethday

Augutht 11th

Wednethday

Augutht 12th

Thurthday

Augutht 13th

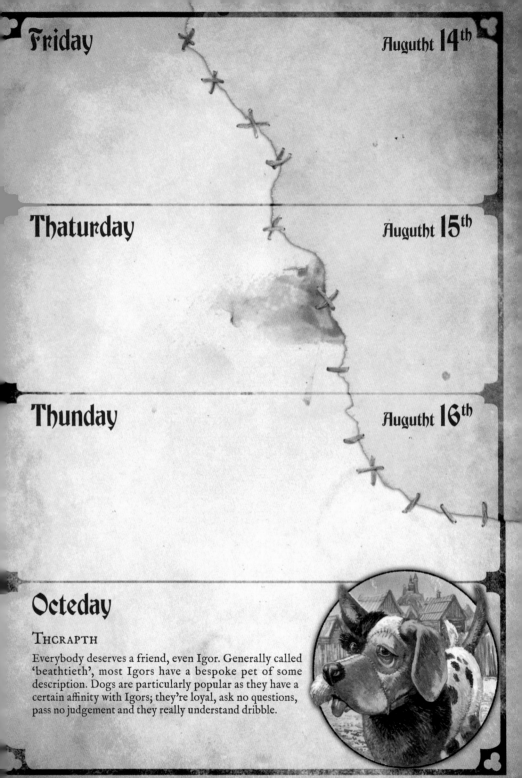

Friday

Augutht **14**th

Thaturday

Augutht **15**th

Thunday

Augutht **16**th

Octeday

Thcrapth

Everybody deserves a friend, even Igor. Generally called 'beathtieth', most Igors have a bespoke pet of some description. Dogs are particularly popular as they have a certain affinity with Igors; they're loyal, ask no questions, pass no judgement and they really understand dribble.

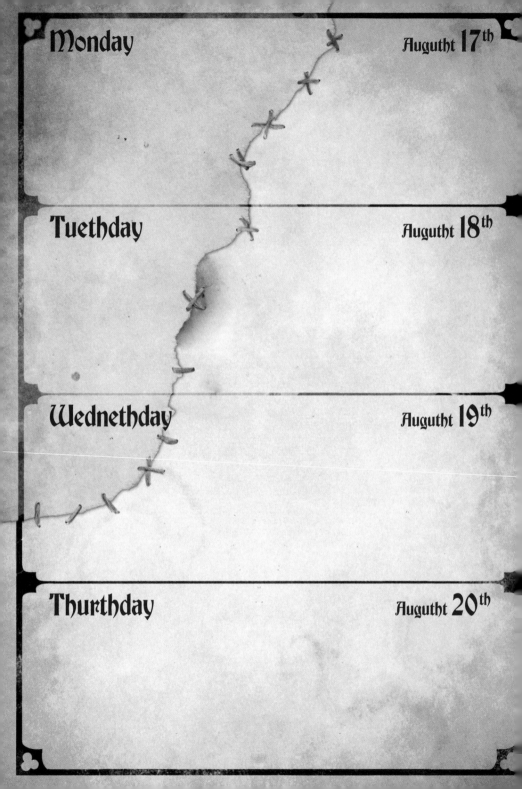

Monday

Auguht 17th

Tuethday

Augutht 18th

Wednethday

Augutht 19th

Thurthday

Augutht 20th

Friday

Augutht **21**tht

Thaturday

Augutht **22**nd

Thunday

Augutht **23**rd

Octeday

PATCHETH

'Patcheth' is a bit of a local celebrity in the town of Bugs. He now belongs to Igor, though he was first put together by Igor's great great grandfather, Igor, early in the Century of the Three Lice. Patcheth is one of a litter which suffered a terrible threshing accident. Igor did his best to save them all, but in the end he made 8, out of 10, cats.

Monday

Tuethday

Wednethday

Thurthday

Brebb & Leppis Day

Friday

Augutht **28**th

Thaturday

Augutht **29**th

Thunday

Augutht **30**th

Head of the River (running race with boats on the Ankh)

Octeday

MEMO

From: The Head of Human Resources, We R Igors,
The Rathaus, Bad Schüschein, Uberwald

To: We R Igors,
Elm Street Ankh-Morpork

Daily life in Ankh-Morpork may come as a surprise to inexperienced Igors taking up their first post in the metropolis. No more the silent and bosky forests of the Homeland where the only sounds are the distant thud of a woodman's axe, interrupted occasionally by a strangled cry when a misdirected swing removes the woodman's limb. Here in Ankh-Morpork the background sounds of the busy city can be overwhelming and opportunities to serve the populous wait at every corner. But we must tread carefully; the sensibility of the indigenous inhabitants is such that we should not rush in to gather nature's bounty without consideration of local traditions and beliefs. Neither should we assume that our pursuit of self-improvement will be shared by everyone we meet.

The attached document *'An Igor's Guide to Behaviour in an Urban Environment'* has been prepared in response to concerns raised by Ankh-Morpork residents, religions, commercial operations and Guild members.

We would be grateful if you could ensure that a copy of this guide is given to every Igor arriving in the City along with the usual information about laboratory and icehouse space, and lists of approved suppliers.

AN IGOR'S GUIDE TO
BEHAVIOUR
IN AN URBAN ENVIRONMENT

ACCIDENT IN A PUBLIC PLACE:

Saving life is the first imperative, but the victim may not be aware of your skills and misunderstand your intentions. It is often better to allow them to be taken to the nearest hospital where the resident Igor will attend. Should the accident result in fatalities, always get written permission from next of kin before removing any corpses or parts thereof. Animals injured or killed at the scene will have an owner; seek written permission before removing the bodies. Use your 'Igor Aware' card to stake your claim.

CRIME SCENE:

Always check with the City Watch before entering a crime scene to make sure that all forensic material has been collected before you touch anything. A grieving family may not react kindly to the sight of a group of Igors equipped with ice boxes following the procession. Be sympathetic to their feelings. Hanging around cemeteries does nothing for our image and, anyway, most of the inhabitants are well past their 'use by' date.

ABATTOIRS:

Just stay away.

TEMPLES AND
RELIGIOUS OBSERVANCE:

Beware! Gods can be jealous of their sacrificial offerings. There is often a conflict between religious belief and Igor practices. Avoid any temples where bodily resurrection is part of the faith.

LIGHTNING RODS:

Do not fix lightning rods to your landlord's premises without permission. Clacks towers are private property and the fixing of any device is strictly prohibited.

GUILD TRADITION
AND PRACTICE:

The Guild of Embalmers has long enjoyed a monopoly on the collection and preservation of cadavers in Ankh-Morpork and providing you leave them sufficient remains of the remains to bury there should not be a problem. In addition, an accommodation may be reached whereby, on an ad hoc basis, an Igor's particular skill may be exchanged for left-over or surplus (internal) parts.

The Guild of Thieves is aware of our cultural traditions and activities. However, this may have not permeated to all members and nefarious offers of cadavers or body parts in exchange for cash should be reported to the City Watch immediately.

The Assassin's Guild has a resident Igor who is responsible for all their repeat business. Please do not involve yourself in the resuscitation of their 'inhumation contracts'.

We R Igors

TO WHOM IT MAY CONCERN:
THIS CADAVER
(being in part or whole)
IS THE PROPERTY OF
We R Igors
NO MATERIAL
(including clothing, pocket contents, shoes or loose teeth)
MAY BE REMOVED FROM THE SITE WITHOUT THE EXPRESS PERMISSION OF OUR AGENT OR REPRESENTATIVE.

IGOR AWARE

Butler's Guild

In Ankh-Morpork, having an Igor on your permanent staff is becoming a status symbol among the well-endowed. Opportunities abound for the young Igor who aspires to be a gentleman's gentleman and the Butler's Guild training adds practical domestic skills which are often not employed in the traditional Uberwald household.

Tuethday
Theptember 1[tht]

Wednethday
Theptember 2nd

Thurthday
Theptember 3rd

Friday

Thaturday

Theptember 5th

Thunday

Theptember 6th

Father'th Day (Aus & NZ)

Octeday

Monday
Labor Day (USA & Canada)

Theptember **7**th

Tuethday

Theptember **8**th

Wednethday

Theptember **9**th

Thurthday

Theptember **10**th

Friday

Thaturday

Thunday

Octeday

A HITCH-HIKERS GUIDE TO UBERWALD

As a rule of thumb, if it's on the side of a rural road, you don't pick it up, especially in Uberwald. On these long and treacherous roads however, if you want to make it home in one piece, or at least with the pieces you're most fond of, it's advantageous to have a medical expert on board.

Monday

Unseen University Rag Week

Theptember **14**th

Tuethday

Theptember **15**th

Wednethday

Theptember **16**th

Thurthday

Theptember **17**th

Friday

Thaturday

Thunday

Octeday

Igor's second hand shop in Klotz is a firm favourite with the local farming community. A spare hand when needed and always plenty to choose from.

Monday

Theptember **21**th

Tuethday

Theptember **22**nd

Wednethday

Theptember **23**rd

Thurthday

Theptember **24**th

Friday

Thaturday

Theptember 26th

Thunday

Theptember 27th

Octeday

Igor artifice is legendary and many a family owes their precious heirlooms to the skill of an Igor artisan. Just as a good watch is passed from generation to generation, a good Igor watchmaker has the eyes and hands of at least three experienced craftsmen.

Monday

Queen's Birthday (WA)

Theptember 28th

Tuethday

Theptember 29th

Wednethday

Theptember 30th

IGORINA SEWING CIRCLE

Every WEDNESDAY AFTERNOON in the DIMWELL STREET COMMUNITY HALL

A WEEKLY GET-TOGETHER WHERE SEWING TECHNIQUES
ARE COMPARED AND NEW STITCHES TRIED OUT.

Also dressmaking and embroidery.

The Fairer Theckth

Igorinas are beautiful, well-proportioned young women who traditionally display a decorative scar or row of stitching on face, wrist or ankle. They are the most sought after members of the Igor clan and are now appearing more frequently outside the forests and valleys of Uberwald. Always well dressed, their clothing can seem a little old-fashioned to Ankh-Morpork eyes, nonetheless they look most fetching in their well-fitted gowns, cloaks and dirndls. An Igorina bride is the object of much envy, not to say speculation, among a fellow's companions.

However, it is not all about appearances. Like Igors, they have an inborn aptitude for healing. They tend not to be involved in major surgery (though this is changing) but their skill in nursing is second to none. Igorinas can be found working in most of the city's hospitals as well as running their own clinics. They are artists with a needle and thread and will use 'invisible mending' when requested. A good Igorina is wise enough to know what a gusset is. They also understand that most patients want to be made well, not better.

Igorinas understand that a lot of women do not like the shape they find themselves in; maybe their bust doesn't appeal or their smile is crooked. Never fear! An Igorina knows what to do, discreetly and quickly, while the children are at school. It is accepted, especially by the Gods, that not everyone can be born a goddess, but the local Igorina will know what to do with sympathy and hope.

The Igorina Lying-In Hospital is the best facility of its kind in Ankh-Morpork. All children born there are healthy and without blemish. They also run a domiciliary service for expectant mothers.

As a rule, Igorinas are career women preferring not to spend much time on domestic chores, or cooking. After all they know the way to a man's heart is up and under his ribcage.

Opportunity Knocks
Sometimes with a blunt instrument.

Joining the City Watch here in Ankh-Morpork is becoming a most sought after career choice for the 'young Igor from the old country'. Forensic science is an important aspect of modern policing and this is a job ideally suited to the skills of the Igor. However there is much competition for these posts and it is worth making preparation prior to presenting job applications and attending interviews.

As with all 'backroom' services, the Watch are loathe to spend money, so the more equipment you have yourself the more chance you have of being given a position.

You will need: Several large metal buckets, glass jars and demijohns, metal dinner plates, yards of rubber tubing, bowls and of course your usual equipment as 'an Igor on the make' – or at least 'on the repair'. You might also add to this a good heavy-duty saw, a crowbar, a few chisels and of course a spade or three. It is worth noting that garden trowels perform capital service in the area of exhumation or incidents involving elephants and circus dwarves. Do not display too much enthusiasm over having access to fresh cadavers.

When introduced to the scene of crime it is not a good idea, when examining the body, to declare: "I thay, thith ith a nithe little kidney, thertainly thome life left in thith". The organ in question is probably required as evidence and if any of the deceased relatives overhear your remark they will undoubtedly complain. Show organisational skills; make notes at the scene of the crime, and pay particular attention to the accurate labelling of cadavers and parts thereof. Do not go off duty with any extremities, limbs or soft floppy parts in jars where anyone can see them without signing them out first. Your duties will, in the main, consist of identifying remains and helping establish cause of death. Have an open mind and always get hold of the brain if you can – it may prove useful. Keep your own eyes open, others can be put in jars just as soon as they are no longer required on the scene. Your knowledge of anatomy and ability to identify a species from a few drops of blood will enable you to offer a real and valuable service to the Watch. You will also be expected to supply such services as may be occasioned by the normal 'hurly burly' of life amongst miscreants armed with edged weapons.

They say it's a man's/dwarf's/troll's/were-wolf's/vampire's/golem's life in the Watch. Well, it's an Igor's too, and a good career that will give you many parts to play (with). Enjoy!

Friday

October 2nd

Thaturday

October 3rd

Thunday

October 4th

Daylight Savings Time starts (Aus)

Octeday

Monday

Labour Day (ACT, NSW, SA)

October **5**th

Tuethday

Soul Cake Day

October **6**th

Wednethday

October **7**th

Thurthday

October **8**th

Friday

October 9th

Thaturday

October 10th

Thunday

October 11th

Octeday

Spider-training is a very acceptable and affordable hobby for any young Igor entering into service. Quality spiderwebs can make or break the ambience of a well-kept house. The Uberwald Grey Vidow is recommended for beginners being an industrious, compliant and above all, affectionate species that thrives in colder climbs.

Monday

Chase Whiskers Day
Thanksgiving Day (Canada)

October 12th

Tuethday

October 13th

Wednethday

October 14th

Thurthday

October 15th

Friday

October **16**th

Thaturday

October **17**th

B.E. Day

Thunday

October **18**th

Octeday

It should never be suggested that Igors have a leaning towards the melodramatic, at least not within earshot.

Monday

October 19th

Tuethday

October 20th

Wednethday

October 21tht

Thurthday

October 22nd

Friday

October 23rd

Thaturday

October 24th

Thunday

October 25th

Sto Plains Tiddly-Winks Finals
British Summer Time ends (UK)

Octeday

HEALTH AND THAFETY

Like a rubber safety-stake to the heart of tradition, Health and Safety has arrived in the Homeland. The Uberwaldian way of life has survived the rise and fall of the Dark Empire, it shrugged off hordes of ice giants, the Fifth Elephant barely left a dent, but there is nothing more demoralising than 'The Man' fiddling with your secret passageway.

Monday
Labour Day (NZ)

October **26**th

Tuethday

October **27**th

Wednethday

October **28**th

Thurthday

October **29**th

Friday

Thaturday

October 31tht

Halloween
Samhain

Thunday

November 1tht

Daylight Saving Time ends (USA & Canada)

Octeday

By all means let Igor mix your drink, just remember that he
doesn't mix his metaphors. A Bloody Mary* mixed by your Igor
might well be the very thing.

*known locally as a Bloody Murder, though we're
promised that's due to the high price of tomatoes.

Monday

November 2nd

Tuethday

November 3rd

Wednethday

November 4th

Thurthday

November 5th

Guy Fawkes' Day

Friday

November **6**th

Thaturday

November **7**th

Thunday

November **8**th

Octeday

IGOR HALL OF FAME
Field of Music

The high point of the Duschen-Duschen Music Festival; Igor performs 'The Organ Concerto for Three Hands' by Magrato.

Monday
November 9th

Tuethday
November 10th

Wednethday
November 11th

Remembrance Day

Thurthday
November 12th

Friday

November 13th

Thaturday

November 14th

Thunday

November 15th

Octeday

IGOR HALL OF FAME
Furtherment of Civilisation Through Culinary Bio-Artificing

Man invented the wheel and stole fire from the Gods. Man built the Great Wall of the Agatean Empire. He split the Thaum, put a man on the moon and even fathomed the rules of crockett, but by cross-breeding a potato with a particularly common trout, it took an Igor to invent instant fish and chips.

Monday

Tattogey Week

November 16th

Tuethday

November 17th

Wednethday

November 18th

Thurthday

November 19th

Friday

November 20th

Thaturday

November 21tht

Thunday

November 22nd

Octeday

Frogs Legs

People eat thethe in Genua. What a wathte!

Monday

November 23rd

Tuethday

November 24th

Wednethday

November 25th

Thurthday

Thanksgiving Day (USA)

November 26th

Friday
November 27th

Thaturday
November 28th

Thunday
November 29th

Octeday

Rapid Response Igor provides succour where needed or a speedy removal of remains where not – 'Delivery in 30 minutes, or your pieces are free!'.

THE ELM STREET

Drop Off Centre and SPORTS & SOCIAL CLUB

A MEETING PLACE FOR IGORS IN ANKH-MORPORK WHERE THEY CAN GET TOGETHER WITH OTHER MEMBERS OF THE CLAN AND ENJOY A BUSY PROGRAMME OF SPORTING ACTIVITIES, FORMAL DINNER DANCES, EXCURSIONS AND EDUCATIONAL LECTURES AND DEMONSTRATIONS.

☛ YOUNG IGORS are encouraged to attend the 'SHOW AND TELL' meetings on Saturday mornings and can have a go in the 'lucky dip' afterwards.

☛ TUESDAY EVENING seminars, which are preceded by a 'BRING & EXCHANGE' session, allow Igors who work in isolation a chance to catch up with improved techniques and see demonstrations of new equipment.

☛ THE SUMMER HIGHLIGHT of the year is the ANNUAL SPORTS DAY which is held on The Cockled Moor. Keen young Igors spend all year preparing themselves for the rigours of the one hundred yard hurtle and the cross country lurch, as well as the more usual three-legged and 'eye and spoon' races. Traditional 'Old Country' skills such as speed dust-laying and the squeakiest door, are also included. The Blintz Memorial Trophy is awarded to the best all-rounder.

☛ THE CLUB has its own foot-the-ball team, but please remember that this is a team game and NOT an anatomical excursion. Regrettably, the practice of transferring choice parts rather than whole players, in and out of the team, has caused them to be disqualified for the current season.

☛ A GRAND GALA BALL is held at Hogswatch, His Grace, Lord Vetinari traditionally honours the occasion with his presence.

Old vampire family requires traditionally trained Igor as personal servant and for cellar duties. Long contract.

Count Von Shaudenfraude, Splitz, Überwald

NOT A MAD SCIENTIST AT ALL
REQUIRES IGOR WITH A HEAD FOR HEIGHTS. OWN LIGHTNING GATHERING EQUIPMENT ESSENTIAL.
Weekends only.
APPLY DR VON HARSCHKINCH, HAMMER HOUSE, PIN GATE, ANKH-MORPORK

Count Wulf Snaphausen requires Igor as valet and groom
Must like dogs. No pets.
Apply to housekeeper, Mrs Pouncewell, Bonk, Überwald.

REFORMED VAMPIRE FAMILY
(Black Ribboners and proud)

NEWLY DOMICILED IN ANKH-MORPORK REQUIRE IGORINA EXPERIENCED IN CHILD CARE FOR NURSERY DUTIES.

REFERENCES REQUIRED.

APPLY IN WRITING TO: MADAME DARLINK, MOREOVER LAWNS, A-M

Exciting opportunity to join *Igors R Us Co-operative*. A large new cold store and re-cycling warehouse facility available for immediate occupancy in *King's Industrial Compound, New Ankh*.
EASY ACCESS TO RAILWAY TERMINUS.

Dunliving Retirement Home, Last Street, seeks part time Igor for 'MAKE DO AND MEND REPAIRS'.

Top Class Establishment requires Igor butler.

In addition to the usual skills the successful candidate will have 'City and Butler's Guild' qualifications as well as experience of working in a social environment.

Igor currently working for respectable family in AM would like to return to the Old Country for traditional pursuits and employment. Will exchange with Igor wishing to experience the metropolitan lifestyle.
Contact Igor.

Good all-rounder, watchmaker's eyes and footballer's leg seeks Athletes foot for sports day.

LADY SYBIL HOSPITAL. A VACANCY HAS ARISEN IN THE FRACTURE CLINIC. WOULD SUIT EXPERIENCED IGOR WHO CAN FOLLOW CLINICAL PRACTICE AND NOT USE HIS INITIATIVE.

Uniform provided.
Bring your own dust.

Apply Fidgett's Club, Esoteric Street

Position Wanted
A keen Igor with own equipment and special interest in bio-artificing seeks position with access to secluded and secure heated greenhouse. Willing to help with gardening and general household duties.
Contact Igor in Room 6, No. 5b, Apothecary Walk, AM

To get a head, put your betht foot forward.

Tuethday

Dethember 1^{tht}

Wednethday

Dethember 2nd

Thurthday

Dethember 3rd

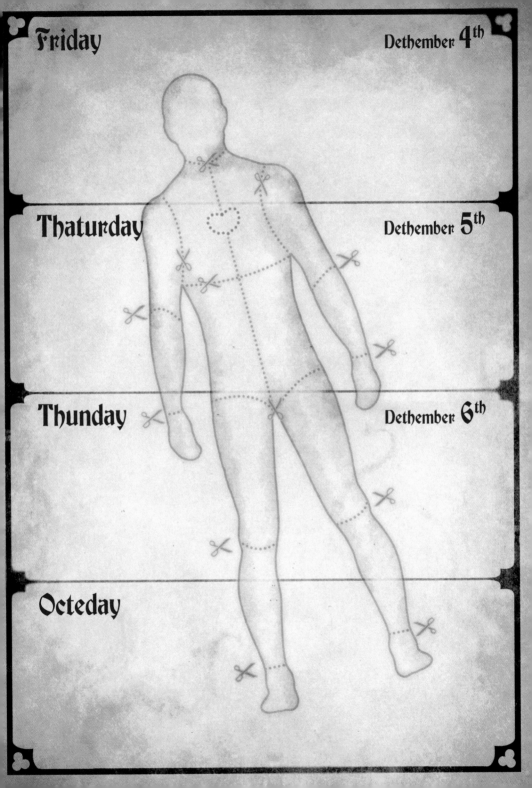

Friday

Thaturday

Thunday

Octeday

Monday

Tuethday

Wednethday

Thurthday

Friday

Thaturday

Thunday

Octeday

IGOR HALL OF FAME
Field of Sport

After receiving a lifetime ban from the Sto Plains Professional
Three-legged-racing Syndicate and the Offlerian Amateur
Kick-boxing Team for unfair advantage, he turned his hand
to foot-the-ball – the only amateur sport where sportsmanship
is still actively discouraged.

Monday

Dethember 14th

Tuethday

Dethember 15th

Wednethday

Dethember 16th

Thurthday

Dethember 17th

Friday

Thaturday

Thunday

Octeday

Monday

Tuethday

Yule (Winter Solstice)

Dethember 22nd

Wednethday

Dethember 23rd

Thurthday

Chrithtmath Eve

Dethember 24th

Friday

Thaturday

Thunday

Octeday

HAPPY HOGTHWATCH

An Igor's festive board is legendary, fusion food being something of a 'thpethiality'. The result is the only known roast from which one may be offered leg, breast, wing, rump, chop or chitterlings.

Monday

Dethember 28th

Tuethday

Dethember 29th

Wednethday
Hogswatcheve

Dethember 30th

Thurthday
Hogswatchnight

Dethember 31tht

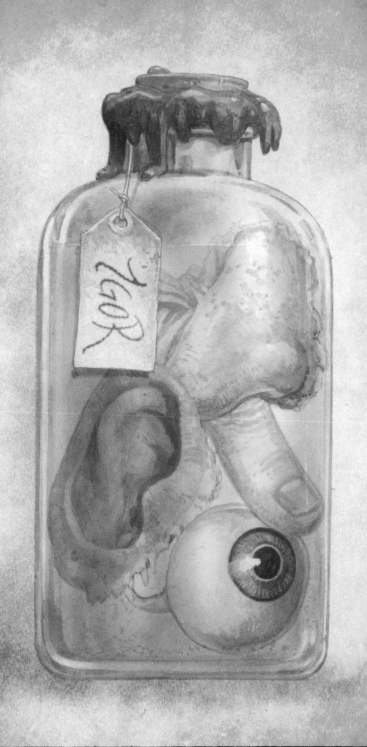

Two Thousand 2016 and Sixteen A.D.

January

M	T	W	T	F	S	S
				1	2	3
4	5	6	7	8	9	10
11	12	13	14	15	16	17
18	19	20	21	22	23	24
25	26	27	28	29	30	31

February

M	T	W	T	F	S	S
1	2	3	4	5	6	7
8	9	10	11	12	13	14
15	16	17	18	19	20	21
22	23	24	25	26	27	28
29						

March

M	T	W	T	F	S	S
	1	2	3	4	5	6
7	8	9	10	11	12	13
14	15	16	17	18	19	20
21	22	23	24	25	26	27
28	29	30	31			

April

M	T	W	T	F	S	S
				1	2	3
4	5	6	7	8	9	10
11	12	13	14	15	16	17
18	19	20	21	22	23	24
25	26	27	28	29	30	

May

M	T	W	T	F	S	S
						1
2	3	4	5	6	7	8
9	10	11	12	13	14	15
16	17	18	19	20	21	22
23/30	24/31	25	26	27	28	29

June

M	T	W	T	F	S	S
		1	2	3	4	5
6	7	8	9	10	11	12
13	14	15	16	17	18	19
20	21	22	23	24	25	26
27	28	29	30			